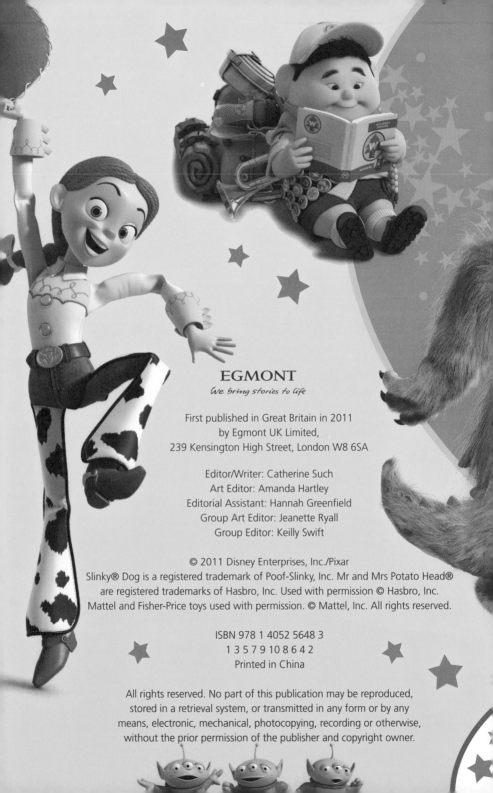

EGMONT
We bring stories to life

First published in Great Britain in 2011
by Egmont UK Limited,
239 Kensington High Street, London W8 6SA

Editor/Writer: Catherine Such
Art Editor: Amanda Hartley
Editorial Assistant: Hannah Greenfield
Group Art Editor: Jeanette Ryall
Group Editor: Keilly Swift

ISBN 978 1 4052 5648 3
1 3 5 7 9 10 8 6 4 2
Printed in China

DISNEY · PIXAR
HOLIDAY ANNUAL

This Holiday Annual belongs to

DISNEY · PIXAR
HOLIDAY ANNUAL

DISNEY · PIXAR — TOY STORY 3

Playtime 8
A New Friend 12
Playtime Pal 20
Buzz Puzzles 22
Toy Time 24
Cowgirl Capers 26
Daycare Differences 28

DISNEY · PIXAR — WALL·E

WALL·E's World 30
Space Race 32
Spaceship Spot 34
Bot Match 36
Robot Fun 38

DISNEY · PIXAR — FINDING NEMO

Under the Sea 40
A Tasty Tale 44
Underwater Fun 52
Ocean Activities 54
Fishy Fun 56
Dory Dash 58

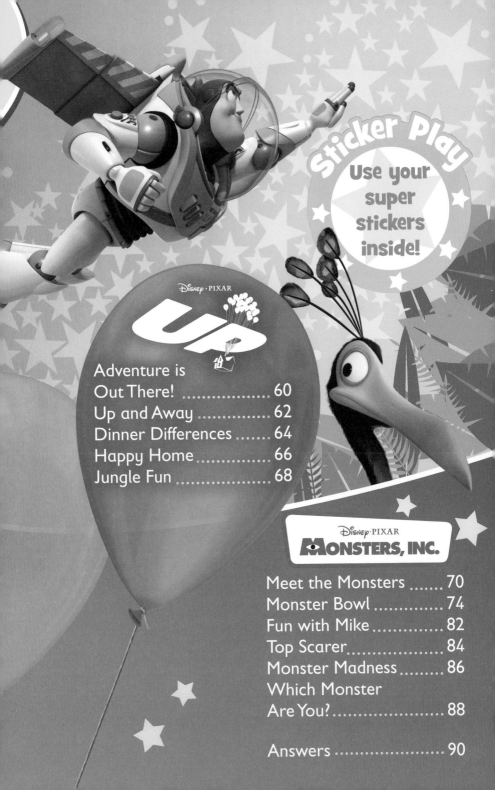

DISNEY · PIXAR

UP

Adventure is
Out There! 60
Up and Away 62
Dinner Differences 64
Happy Home 66
Jungle Fun 68

DISNEY · PIXAR

MONSTERS, INC.

Meet the Monsters 70
Monster Bowl 74
Fun with Mike 82
Top Scarer 84
Monster Madness 86
Which Monster
Are You? 88

Answers 90

Playtime ...

Let's find out more about Woody, Buzz and the gang and meet some of the toys from Sunnyside Daycare.

Buzz Lightyear

Space Ranger Buzz is bold, fearless and brave. He's very proud of his laser beam and pop-out wings.

Jessie

Jessie loves adventure. She's a kind-hearted cowgirl who's always ready to help a toy in need.

Woody

Sheriff Woody is Andy's favourite toy. He's kind and loyal and always makes sure no toy gets left behind.

9

Rex and Hamm

Dinosaur Rex worries about everything. Piggy-bank Hamm thinks he knows it all!

Mr Potato Head has lost an ear! Can you find it somewhere on these pages?

Answer on page 90.

10

Lotso and Friends

Lotso is in charge at Sunnyside Daycare. But the cuddly, strawberry-scented bear isn't always as friendly as he looks!

Sticker Play

Stick a star-shaped sticker next to your favourite character.

A New Friend

1 One day, Hamm rushed over to the other toys in a panic. "Run for your lives, the modelling clay has escaped from its box!" he cried.

2 Suddenly, they spotted the giant blob of soft, multi-coloured squidge crawling across the room towards them. "It's coming to get us!" cried Rex.

3 The toys all tried to run in different directions, but the big, silent blob quickly changed its form. It spread out into a long, snake-like shape and circled them.

4 "Leave us alone, rainbow mutant!" yelled Buzz. The blob didn't make a sound, it just closed in around them. "It's going to swallow us whole!" cried Hamm.

5 Bullseye tried to run over the top of it but his feet sunk into the squidge. He was stuck! Suddenly, a piece of the blob broke off and moved up on to his back.

6 "Don't worry, Bullseye! We'll help you!" Woody cried out to his friend. More and more bits of the blob were breaking off and heading towards each toy.

7 Then Rex looked over at Bullseye. The bit of blob on his back had moulded itself into a smiling rider. "Look, the blob just wants to play!" Rex cheered.

8 The toys saw that each bit of the blob had changed into something exciting for them to play with. "What a great new friend!" laughed Woody.

Sticker Play
Add a sticker when you have finished reading the story.

Put your sticker here.

The End

Playtime Pal

Who does Jessie want to play with? Use the clues below to work out the answer.

He isn't wearing a hat.

He has a tail.

He doesn't have a saddle.

He is green.

Jessie wants to play with

....
Write your answer here.

Answer on page 90.

Buzz Puzzles

Join Buzz on his mission to tackle these tricky teasers.

1

Can you spot three differences between these two aliens?

B	U	Z	Z	B
U	B	Z	B	U
Z	U	B	U	Z
Z	B	U	Z	Z
B	U	Z	Z	U

SPACE RANGER LIGHTYEAR

2

How many times does BUZZ appear in this wordsearch? Write your answer here.

3

Can you guide Buzz through the maze to rescue Jessie? Make sure you don't run into Lotso on the way!

START

FINISH

Disney · PIXAR

TOY STORY 3

Toy Time

Which Toy Story 3 characters can you see below?

Spot 'em!

Tick the box when you spot each toy in the big picture.

Woody

Jessie

Buzz

24

Who is your favourite character?

....
Write your answer here.

Sticker Play

Add a sheriff badge sticker when you have finished.

Put your sticker here.

(**Mr Potato Head**)　(**Bullseye**)　(**Barbie**)

25

Cowgirl Capers

Yee-haa! Can you help Jessie complete the fun activities on these pages?

Jessie is sorting out Bullseye's horseshoes. Can you count how many of each colour she has?

Use your brightest pens to colour this picture of Jessie giving Bullseye a great big hug.

Write your answers here.

Sticker Play

Add a horseshoe sticker when you have finished.

Put your sticker here.

Daycare Differences

Can you spot five differences between these pictures of the toys at Sunnyside Daycare?

Sticker Play

Add a sticker
each time
you spot a
difference.

Answers on page 90.

DISNEP · PIXAR
WALL·E

WALL·E'S World

Let's zoom forward to **2805** and meet up with **WALL·E** and his friends ...

WALL·E

Hard-working WALL·E is curious and kind-hearted. He loves collecting interesting objects ... even when he doesn't know what they are!

EVE

Sleek robot EVE was sent to Earth to scan for signs of life. She is determined to do a good job wherever she goes.

Use the dots to help you colour this picture of planet Earth.

M-O

M-O loves cleaning! He works hard to keep the *Axiom* star liner looking brand new.

Sticker Play

Stick a planet Earth sticker next to your favourite character.

Space Race

How quickly can you help WALL·E and EVE solve these exciting space puzzles?

1

Spot the odd one out in each row. Write your answers in the boxes.

2

What four space words can you find in this word wheel?

rocketstarsmoonplanet

Can you find this planet hidden somewhere on these pages?

Sticker Play

Add a sticker when you spot the planet.

Put your sticker here.

WALL·E

Answers on page 90.

Spaceship Spot

WALL·E is in the escape pod on the Axiom. Can you spot the details in the red circle in the big picture?

BnL
Colour
WALL·E!

Colour a star
each time you
find a detail.

a

b

c

d

e

35

Bot Match

The bots need your help!
Can you match each one
to its correct shadow?

a

b

c

d

e

Answers on page 90.

Robot Fun

WALL·E and EVE are exploring Earth. Join in their adventure by completing these activities.

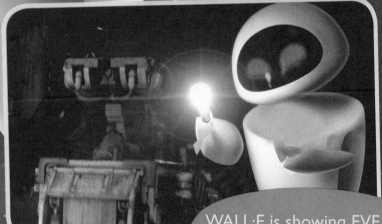

WALL·E is showing EVE his trash treasures. Which jigsaw piece isn't from the scene?

a

b

c

Answer on page 90.

Under the Sea

Let's take a trip to the bottom of the ocean to find out more about Nemo and his friends.

Nemo

Clownfish Nemo is curious and adventurous. He loves to explore and always wants to know what's around the next reef.

Marlin

Nemo's dad Marlin is a big worrier, but he's the best dad a fish could ask for.

Sheldon

Seahorse Sheldon is Nemo's best friend. They have lots of fun together.

Bruce

Bruce may look scary but this big shark is a softie at heart. Fish are friends, not food!

Dory

Forgetful Dory is kind and caring. She has lots of friends and can even speak 'whale'!

Crush and Squirt

Laid-back turtles Crush and Squirt enjoy chilling out while riding the East Australian Current.

Can you rearrange the letters on these bubbles to make a watery word? Write your answer in the space below.

Answer on page 90.

Sticker Play

Stick a jellyfish sticker next to your favourite character.

s a s
l p h

_____ _____ _____ _____ _____ _____

A Tasty

1 One day, Marlin took Bob, Ted and Phil for a gentle swim in the shallows. "Isn't this great?" Marlin said to his friends. "We really should do this more often."

Tale

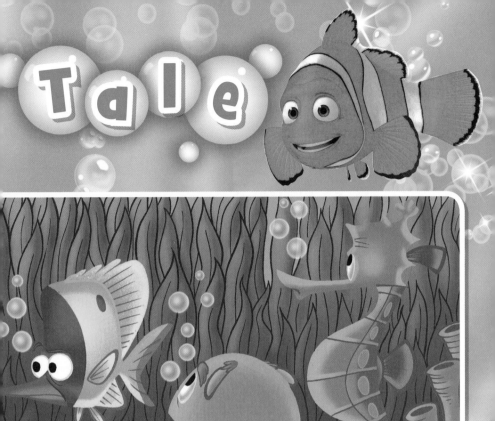

2 Soon though, the tide started to go out and the sea level lowered. Now, some very tall seaweed, which they couldn't swim over, blocked their way home.

3 "Let's go around the seaweed," suggested Marlin. He led his friends to the edge of the ocean shelf. "It looks quiet," said Phil. "Follow me!" said Marlin, bravely.

4 Suddenly, three dark shapes with sharp teeth appeared. It was Bruce and his friends. "We're going to be eaten alive!" cried Bob, as the shapes swam closer.

5 "Have you eaten yet?" Bruce asked
Marlin. "No, but I am hungry," replied
Marlin. "Us, too," drooled the sharks. Bob,
Ted and Phil began to feel nervous …

© Disney/Pixar

WALL·E + EVE
© Disney/Pixar

© Hasbro, Inc.

Mr. and Mrs. Potato Head®

SHERIFF

WOODY

6 "You see, when sharks get hungry,"
Chum told them, "they've got to eat."
Suddenly, the sharks lunged forwards. "No!"
cried Bob, Ted and Phil in horror.

7 When Bob, Ted and Phil finally opened their eyes, they saw Bruce chewing on a mouthful of seaweed. "What did you think he was going to do? Eat you?" asked Marlin.

8 "It did cross my mind," replied Phil, watching Bruce chew a path through the seaweed. "Thanks, Bruce!" said Marlin, leading his nervous friends home.

Sticker Play

Add a sticker when you have finished reading the story.

Put your sticker here.

The End

Underwater Fun

Mr Ray is taking his class on a field trip. Join in by completing these activities.

1
How many classmates are swimming with Mr Ray?

2
Can you colour Mr Ray?

3

Use Bruce's code above to work out what fish are to him. Fill in your answer below.

Fish are ...

Ocean Activities

Help Dory match her fish friends into pairs, then add some bright colours to Nemo and Marlin.

a

b

c

d

Sticker Play

Add a sticker when you have finished.

Put your sticker here.

e

f

Answers on page 91.

Fishy Fun

Nemo and his friends are swimming at the reef. Jump in and answer these underwater questions.

1 How many friends can you count?

2 Which way is Tad swimming?

Left or right

Sticker Play
Use your stickers to add some more fish to this scene.

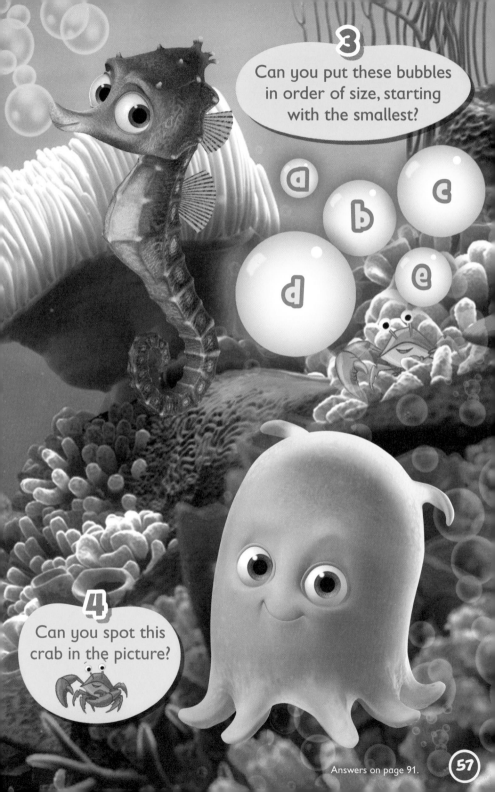

3

Can you put these bubbles in order of size, starting with the smallest?

a

b

c

d

e

4

Can you spot this crab in the picture?

Dory Dash

Dory is going to meet Nemo but she's forgotten the way! Can you guide her through the maze to her friend?

START

Top Tip
Make sure Dory passes all the clams on her way!

Which Marlin is the odd one out?

Answers on page 91.

Adventure is Out There!

Let's head to Paradise Falls to find out more about the stars of Up.

Russell

Junior Wilderness Explorer Russell loves earning badges. He's always keen to lend a hand.

How many balloons can you count floating around these pages?

Kevin

Kevin is a very tall, very rare jungle bird who's actually a girl! She can run very fast and loves eating chocolate.

Carl

Seventy-eight-year-old Carl is a grump. He likes routine and hates it when things don't go according to plan.

Dug

Talking dog Dug is loyal and loveable, but he isn't the smartest pooch in the pack!

Sticker Play

Stick an explorer sticker next to your favourite character.

Answer on page 91.

Up and Away

Help Carl and Russell collect balloons
and float to Paradise Falls.

Which path should
Carl and Russell
follow to collect the
most balloons?

a

b

c

Colour the balloons to help the house float away!

Answer on page 91.

63

Dinner Differences

Carl and Russell are tucking
into a yummy meal in Muntz's lair.
Can you spot five differences
in the picture on the right?

Sticker Play

Add a sticker each time you spot a difference.

Put your sticker here.

Put your sticker here.

Put your sticker here.

Put your sticker here.

Put your sticker here.

Put your sticker here.

Happy Home

Russell is visiting Carl at home.
Can you find the objects on
the right in the room?

Spot 'em!

Tick a box as you spot each object.

Add some colour to brighten up Carl's chair.

67

Jungle Fun

Russell is on an adventure.
Join him by completing these
exciting activities.

1

Can you match
these Wilderness
Explorer badges
into pairs?

a

b

c

d

e

f

a **b** **c**

2 Can you spot which one of these is Carl's real house? It's the odd one out.

3 Use the dots to help you colour in this picture of Kevin.

Answers on page 91.

69

Meet the Monsters

Life's a scream at the Monsters, Inc. factory! Let's find out more about our scary friends.

Boo

Little Boo is lively and curious and loves her monster friends. Everything they do makes her giggle!

Mike

Funny Mike enjoys making his friends laugh. There's never a dull moment with him around!

Sulley

Big, furry Sulley is the top scarer at Monsters, Inc. But off duty, he's the nicest monster around.

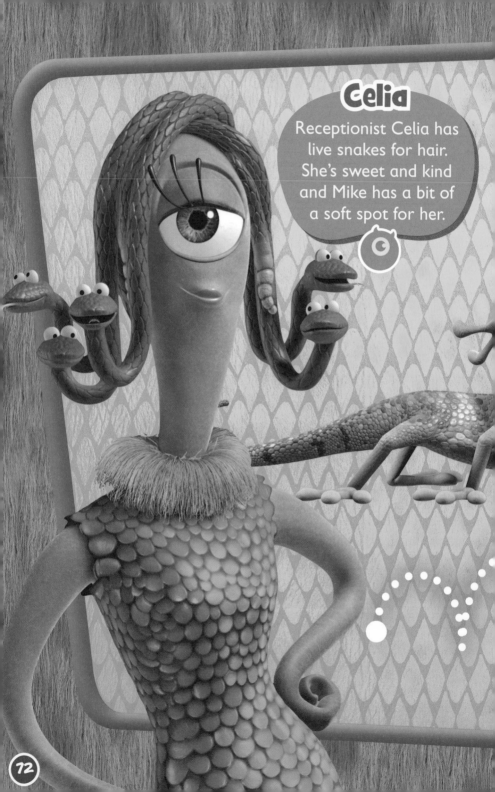

Celia

Receptionist Celia has live snakes for hair. She's sweet and kind and Mike has a bit of a soft spot for her.

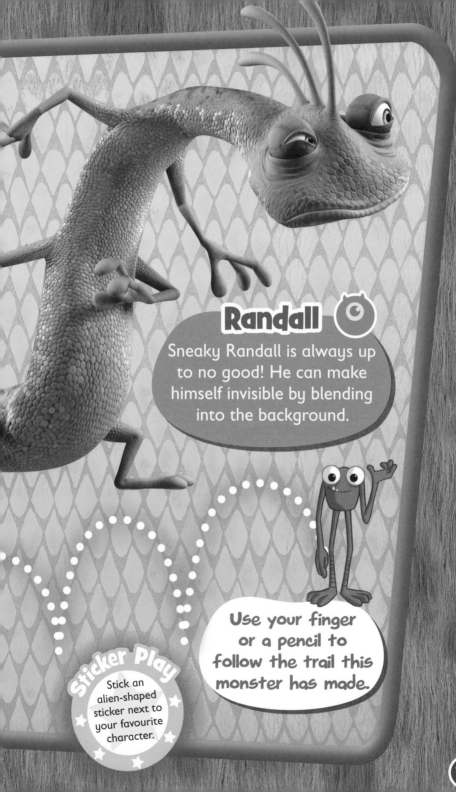

Randall

Sneaky Randall is always up to no good! He can make himself invisible by blending into the background.

Use your finger or a pencil to follow the trail this monster has made.

Sticker Play
Stick an alien-shaped sticker next to your favourite character.

Monster Bowl

1 One day, Sulley was having a great scare shift at Monsters, Inc. "Look at all the screams Sulley's collected!" Mike proudly told a group of Scarers.

2 "Ummm, I don't see any scream canisters, Mike," one Scarer replied. He was right. The canisters had been taken by sneaky Randall!

3 Mike couldn't see Randall, because he had blended in with the Scare Floor. "Hey!" Mike shouted as loud as he could, "Someone stop those runaway canisters!"

4 Just then, Sulley arrived back on the Scare Floor. "How are things going so far, Mike?" he asked. "Not so well, Sulley, our screams are escaping!" Mike cried.

5 "No problem, pal! Get ready for a fun ride," Sulley replied. He picked up Mike, just like a bowling ball. "Move out of the way, Scarers!" he laughed.

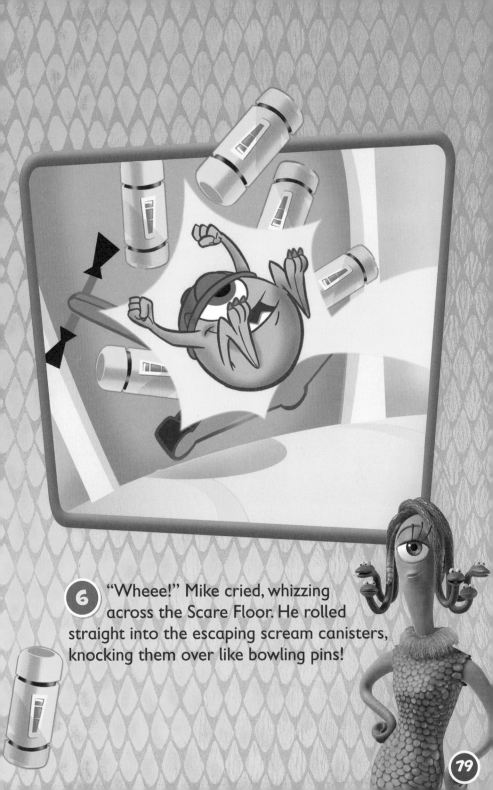

6 "Wheee!" Mike cried, whizzing across the Scare Floor. He rolled straight into the escaping scream canisters, knocking them over like bowling pins!

7 Randall was trapped under the canisters that Mike had knocked over! "Thanks, Randall. I needed the bowling practice for after work!" Sulley joked.

8 That evening, Sulley and Mike went to the Monster Bowling Alley. "Bowling is great fun," Sulley said to his friend. "Yeah, especially when I'm the ball!" Mike agreed.

The End

Sticker Play

Add a sticker when you have finished reading the story.

Put your sticker here.

Fun with Mike

Mike is taking a break from scaring to complete these monster activities. Can you help him out?

Put your sticker here.
BOO

Put your sticker here.
MIKE

Put your sticker here.
CELIA

Find these names in the wordsearch below.

Put your sticker here.
SULLEY

Put your sticker here.
RANDALL

Sticker Play
Add a sticker each time you find a name.

I	F	L	C	R	O	S	K	I
C	E	L	I	A	P	E	S	B
E	A	U	U	N	X	M	H	O
C	T	L	N	D	R	I	O	L
R	A	N	T	A	L	K	E	E
E	Y	M	B	L	R	E	S	A
A	B	O	O	L	J	R	O	F
M	T	N	S	U	L	L	E	Y
S	M	I	E	K	I	N	Z	F

Add some monster colours to this picture of super scarers, Mike and Sulley.

Top Scarer

Who is the scariest monster on the Scare Floor? Follow the trails below to find out!

a

b

Monster Tip

The monster with the fullest scream canister is the scariest. Use the red indicator to help you.

Answer on page 91.

Monster Madness

Mike loves making everyone laugh! Join in the fun with these brilliant activities.

1

Can you match each monster to their glasses?

Which Monster Are You?

Play this fun game to find out which monster you're most like.

1 Who would be your best friend?

2 Which monster snack would you choose?

3 Which toy would you play with?

Mostly Green

You and Mike could be twins! You're full of fun and know how to make your friends laugh.

Mostly Blue

You are just like Sulley. You're kind and thoughtful and always put your friends first.

Mostly Red

You're quiet and caring, just like Celia. Friends know they can always count on you.

If you ticked one of each colour, you're lucky enough to be like all the monsters!

Answers

Page 10-11

Playtime ...
Mr Potato Head's ear is above Lotso.

Page 20-21

Playtime Pal
Jessie wants to play with Rex.

Page 22-23

Buzz Puzzles
1.

2. Buzz appears 6 times.

3.

Page 26-27

Cowgirl Capers
Green = 5, yellow = 3, red = 4, blue = 2.

Page 28-29

Daycare Differences

Page 32-33

Space Race
1. b, c, a.
2. Stars, moon, planets, rocket.

Page 36-37

Bot Match
1 – e, 2 – d, 3 – a, 4 – b, 5 – c.

Page 38-39

Robot Fun
Jigsaw piece c.

Page 42-43

Under the Sea
Splash.

Page 52-53

Underwater Fun
1. 9.
3. Friends.

Page 54-55

Ocean Activities
a and d, b and f,
c and e.

Page 56-57

Fishy Fun
1. 5.
2. Right.
3. a, e, b, c, d.
3. The crab is behind Pearl.

Page 58-59

Dory Dash

Marlin b is the
odd one out.

Page 60-61

Adventure is Out There!
There are 9 balloons.

Page 62-63

Up and Away
Path c.

Page 64-65

Dinner Differences

Page 68-69

Jungle Fun
1. a and f, b and d,
c and e.
2. Carl's house is b.

Page 82-83

Fun with Mike

Page 84-85

Top Scarer
b – Sulley.

Page 86-87

Monster Madness
1 – d, 2 – c, 3 – b,
4 – a.

Have you seen these

FREE ALIEN CAMERA PLUS SUPER TOY STORY STICKERS

CLICK! CLICK! PICTURES TO VIEW

Disney · PIXAR

NEW TOY STORY MAGAZINE

Join the new characters inside!

Disney · PIXAR

TOY STORY 3

ISSUE 3

COMICS COLOURING GAMES PUZZLES FUN FACTS!

BE PART OF THE TOY STORY ADVENTURE

SPACE RANGER LIGHTYEAR

Free gift with every issue!

Out monthly

great magazines?

FREE Fishing Game

Disney

Disney and Me

Featuring

THE PRINCESS AND THE FROG

Posters

Colouring

Free gift with every issue!

Issue 461

16 JUN – 6 JUL 2010   £2.30

Out every 3 weeks

Both are available from all good newsagents and supermarkets.